THE CACTI

OF

CALIFORNIA

BY

E. YALE DAWSON

WITH PHOTOGRAPHS BY DON SKINNER

UNIVERSITY OF CALIFORNIA PRESS

BERKELEY AND LOS ANGELES 1966

UNIVERSITY OF CALIFORNIA PRESS
BERKELEY AND LOS ANGELES, CALIFORNIA

© 1966 BY THE REGENTS OF THE UNIVERSITY OF CALIFORNIA
LIBRARY OF CONGRESS CATALOG NUMBER: 65-25843
PRINTED IN THE UNITED STATES OF AMERICA

CONTENTS

Note on illustrations — The cover portrays the Beaver Tail Cactus (*Opuntia basilaris*) in the foreground and the Pancake Pear (*Opuntia chlorotica*) in the background. Most of the color photographs are the work of Don Skinner, who also generously provided textual information through his long experience with California cacti. David L. Walkington, of California State College at Fullerton, provided information and photographs for the interior members of the prickly pear group, and Dr. Ralph Philbrick, of the Santa Barbara Botanic Garden, for the coastal species. Several color photographs are from the Homer Rush collection. Photographs of *Opuntia bigelovii* and *Ferocactus acanthodes* were taken by Dallas Clites. Some of the line drawings were reproduced from the early works of George Engelmann, some from *The Cactaceae* by Britton and Rose, and some from the writer's *How to Know the Cacti*, by permission of the Wm. C. Brown Co.

INTRODUCTION

The study of cacti in California has had a long history. Except for the prickly pear of the Atlantic states, known to Linnaeus, and four species from the upper Missouri River described in 1814 as a result of the exploration of the Louisiana Purchase, the first cacti in this country to be known to science came from San Diego. In 1834 Thomas Nuttall, pioneer of western American botany, discovered in the village of San Diego, then little more than the Mexican mission and its Indians, *"Echinocactus viridescens"* and *"Cereus californicus."*

By 1856, through the work of George Engelmann of St. Louis on collections obtained by the Pacific Railroad Survey and the explorations of the Mexican Boundary Commission, knowledge of California cacti was spreading rapidly. By 1919, when the first volume of the monumental monograph on Cactaceae by Britton and Rose was being published, a large body of information on California cacti had accumulated, and our deserts had been extensively explored.

A number of kinds had eluded the botanists, however, and these have continued to be discovered and described down to the present day. A new publication lies before me, just received in the mail, in which a new species of California prickly pear is named. Its characters have been confused or overlooked all these years and only now are clearly recognized. Similarly, the careful exploration of our desert ranges along the Arizona and Mexican boundaries has revealed very recently the occurrence in California of species hitherto known only from these other areas. Two of these are reported for the first time in this handbook. Perhaps you may find still others.

[5]

The more we explore and the more we learn of the cacti, the less certain we become of just how many kinds there are. Most of the species that were discovered many years ago appeared to be distinct from one another, but as collections expanded and observations became more critical, we noted numerous intergradations and intermediate conditions. Thus, where three species had been named earlier, we may now recognize only one, perhaps in three major variable groups that merge. Furthermore, we are increasingly aware that evolution in the cacti is going on before our eyes, that distinct species (and even genera) in nature are occasionally producing crosses that survive and become, in fact, new species. We have sometimes hastened this process by artificial introduction of species from other areas, particularly the Mission Cactus. The resulting hybridization with native species has added many variables to original natural populations.

Some of the difficulties in recognizing species among these variable cacti are related to their widespread distribution and variation in far-flung geographic areas. As a "broad" species may have a varied population in Texas, another in Arizona, and still another in California, so the California plants may scarcely resemble the Texas plants, yet may be linked by intermediates. Interpretations by different botanists of these variations have led to the use of different scientific names in designating the plants; so do not be dismayed if the name used here does not take the form that appears in another book. We have chosen names that, for a local flora, seem most convenient and useful in designating the California plants. A flora of North America would take a different point of view.

WHAT ARE CACTI?

The cacti of California provide an interesting and comprehensive assortment of members of a unique plant family. There are representatives in the driest, hot deserts; others live in foggy coastal scrub, beside high glacial lakes in the sierra, or in moist coniferous forests. But these are not all the habitats occupied by these remarkable plants.

The cacti are exclusively American plants. Although we find them scattered over much of the world today, those outside America have been carried about and planted since the first European saw a cactus when he disembarked with Columbus at Hispaniola. The first cacti brought to Europe were tropical kinds, and, indeed, the Cactaceae are most widespread in the American tropics, both in the dry and the wet. They grow not only in the tropical deserts of Peru, but in some very wet forests, often epiphytic on trees with orchids and bromeliads. They range all the way from Ecuador south into Patagonia and north into central Canada. They are on most of the Caribbean islands; and in the Galápagos Islands they got as far from the continent as 600 miles, but no farther.

The form of the cacti varies as much as the habitat. Some are spiny, woody, deciduous trees which look no more like the usual succulent cactus than does a rosebush, and there are vinelike, climbing forms that may festoon a forest. In short, we cannot always tell a cactus by its shape. All the cacti, however, have a peculiar structure called the areole.

The areoles are the little spots on the stems of cacti from which the spines arise. These specialized growth centers also produce the flowers and new branches. They usually bear one or more distinct spines, but may instead bear wool, hairs, bristles, or microscopic spines called glochids. In the prickly pears and chollas the true nature of the areole may be seen in young growth, for beside each areole of a young branch is a small, fleshy, awl-shaped structure which is really the leaf (fig. 1). The areole is in its axil and

[7]

represents a bud. This little leaf soon falls off, and in many cacti the leaves are not evident except microscopically, but the areole remains as the place at which growth and reproduction take place.

Fig. 1. Young areoles of *Opuntia*, showing spines in axils of awl-shaped leaves.

The flowers of cacti vary greatly in size, color, and form, but they have several characters in common. Except sometimes in our own *Mammillaria dioica*, the flowers are all perfect, having male and female parts. The ovary is inferior; there are numerous stamens; there is a single style with several stigma lobes; the petals and sepals, of indefinite number and little distinction, are called perianth segments (fig. 2). If a succulent plant has these various floral characters as well as the areoles, it is a cactus. Many succulents that are commonly mistaken for cacti (century plants, yuccas, ocotillo, euphorbias, etc.) can easily be distinguished by these features.

Spines provide many of the characters by which cactus species and genera are distinguished. Some areoles contain a single type of spine and others contain several. The areole usually has some kind of sharp, stiff spine, whether straight, curved, hooked, smooth, ribbed, cylindrical, or flattened. The spines are commonly arranged in a central position and (or)

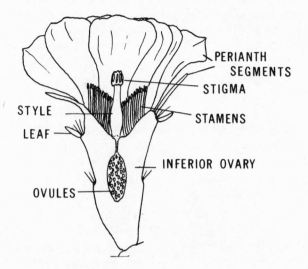

Fig. 2. A flower of *Opuntia* in longitudinal section, showing various parts.

in a radial position (fig. 3). Most genera have spines that are sharply pointed but not barbed. In most of the chollas, however, the spine is minutely barbed and provided with a sheath. In addition to the larger, stiffer spines, there are finer spines. The glochid, which is prevalent in *Opuntia* (fig. 4), is a minutely barbed, almost microscopic spine usually present in large numbers somewhat in the form of a packet. Some areoles contain mainly curly wool, hair, or fine felt forming a kind of pad, sometimes in addition to the heavy spines.

The position of the spines is often important, whether superficial, or on ribs, or crowning low tubercles or nipple-like, elongated tubercules (fig. 5). We have examples of all these types.

Fig. 3.   Two spine clusters, showing central and radial spines.

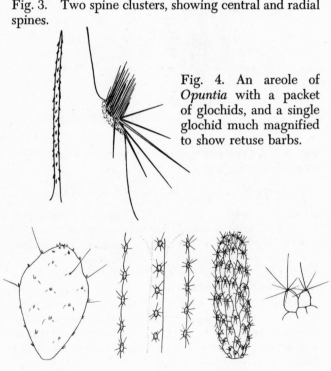

Fig. 4. An areole of *Opuntia* with a packet of glochids, and a single glochid much magnified to show retuse barbs.

Fig. 5. Various positions of spines, left to right: superficial, as in the prickly pears; on ribs, as in the saguaro; on tubercles, as in *Opuntia prolifera;* on nipples, as in *Mammillaria.*

The fruits are of diverse character in various genera. Some are both fleshy and spiny at maturity; others turn dry and shed seeds without going through a stage of soft pulp. Some lose their spines upon ripening and yield a fruit as sweet and innocuous as a strawberry. Others never bear spines and resemble an elongate berry (figs. 6, 25).

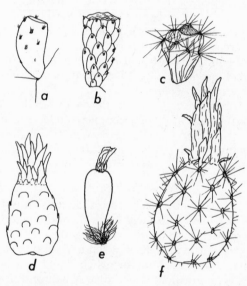

Fig. 6. Various kinds of cactus fruits: a, smooth and fleshy, with glochids (*Opuntia*); b, fleshy, tuberculate, with glochids (*Opuntia*); c. dry tuberculate (*Opuntia*); d. dry scaly (*Ferocactus*); e. fleshy, smooth, spineless (*Mammillaria*); f, fleshy and spiny (*Echinocereus*).

How to Study California Cacti

California wild flowers, including the cacti, are protected by law. In national and state parks, national forests, and in state and some county rights of way, collection of cacti is strictly forbidden. In some counties cacti cannot be collected even on private property without the written permission of the owner. These protective measures have become necessary to insure the perpetuation of these curious plants, many of which were fast disappearing into gardens, and later into trash cans. Living plants may still be collected in some areas by special permit, but usually only for scientific purposes. Most users of this book will study and photograph the cacti, but leave them for the next desert visitor to enjoy.

Photography of cacti in flower is an interesting hobby. The assembly of a complete collection of color slides of California cacti in flower is a challenge to any nature photographer, and his travels to this end are bound to yield exciting experiences.

Where to Find Them

There are several easily accessible areas in southern California in which fairly large numbers of different kinds of cacti may be observed together. For the several species confined to our south coastal region the Cabrillo National Monument on Point Loma, San Diego, is an excellent study area. A nature trail marks various kinds of cacti, and others may be seen within a few hundred yards of the lighthouse.

Most of the interior species of the southernmost desert parts of California may be seen along Highway 78 from Banner down Sentenac Canyon. Another cactus-rich route is Highway 80 from just east of Jacumba to the desert floor near Ocotillo. The lower reaches of the Pines-to-Palms Highway 74 also have cactus species of the Colorado Desert region in abundance.

The cactus flora of the more elevated Mojave Desert is distinct and may best be seen in the Joshua Tree National Monument, which has been set aside for the preservation of the desert flora. From near Whitewater on Highway 10 to Morongo one passes most of the Colorado Desert forms again, but beyond the Little San Bernardino Mountains the cacti of the high Mojave are found. The National Monument has an outstanding natural cactus exhibit area known as Cholla Cactus Garden.

The cactus flora of the far northeastern Mojave Desert, which includes several species not otherwise known within the state, is best seen along or just off Highway 15, the Las Vegas route, near Clark Mountain and the Ivanpah Mountains. Short side trips into such areas as Landfair Valley near Ivanpah may reveal unusual plants.

Several cacti occur in isolated localities in outlying areas. The notes under each plant name in the text will help you to find these localized kinds.

Key to the Genera
and Subgenera of California Cacti

1. Plants gigantic, columnar, 8 to 30 feet tall .. *Carnegiea*
1. Plants smaller, not columnar, usually less than 6 feet tall.2
   2. Plants with flat branches
                        Opuntia, subgenus *Platyopuntia*
   2. Plants globular, or cylindrical,
               or with cylindrical branches 3
3. Plants cylindrical, the branches or main axis many times as long as broad 4
3. Plants globular or short-cylindrical; if branched, the branches only once or a few times as long as broad .. 5
   4. Areoles with glochids; spines usually barbed and with sheaths .... *Opuntia,* subgenus *Cylindropuntia*
   4. Areoles without glochids; spines neither barbed nor with sheaths .... *Bergerocactus*
5. Plants with hooked spines 6
5. Plants with spines straight or curved but not hooked .. 8
   6. Plants 4 inches or more in diameter; hooked spines several inches long .... *Sclerocactus*
   6. Plants, or their branches, less than 3 inches in diameter; hooked spines less than 2 inches long 7
7. Radial spines more than 30; seeds with a corky base
                             Phellosperma
7. Radial spines less than 30; seeds without a corky base
                             Mammillaria
   8. Spines borne on ribs 9
   8. Spines borne on grooved nipples (tubercles)
                             Coryphantha
9. Plants solitary, unbranched or only rarely branched .. 10
9. Plants consisting of clustered heads or branches 11
   10. Spines, at least the centrals, distinctly curved
                             Ferocactus
   10. Spines straight or nearly so .... *Echinomastus*
11. Heads large, more than 6 inches in diameter.*Echinocactus*
11. Heads or branches less than 4 inches in diameter
                             Echinocereus

THE CACTI OF CALIFORNIA

OPUNTIA

Opuntia, our largest cactus genus, includes well over half of the species in the state. The opuntias are distributed almost everywhere cacti grow, from Canada to Patagonia. This large assemblage has two features by which all may be recognized: small awl-shaped leaves are present on young growth; and glochids are borne in the areoles. The several hundred species are divided into two easily recognized subgenera: *Cylindropuntia,* with cylindrical stems; and *Platyopuntia,* in which the stems or joints are flattened pads that are often mistakenly called leaves.

CYLINDROPUNTIA: THE CHOLLAS

Cholla is a Mexican name for the viciously spiny, cylindrical opuntias in which the spines are usually covered by a papery sheath, but are insidiously barbed. The vegetable kingdom has not produced anything else so fearfully armed. But in the desert one thing is worse than any pain of spine in the flesh. It is thirst. I have seen emaciated, dreadfully dehydrated cattle, deprived of water for months in the blistering heat, so mad from thirst that they eat the terrible cholla. They munch these awful morsels of moisture until their lips are pinned together with the spines, and their throats are a veritable pincushion. The spines eventually cause their death.

Pencil Cactus (*Opuntia ramosissima*)

The name "ramosissima," which means "exceedingly much branched," aptly describes this bushy plant. It forms a loose or dense shrub, usually 2 to 3 feet high,

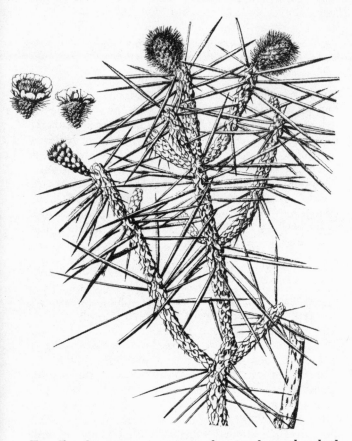

Fig. 7. *Opuntia ramosissima*, showing long, sheathed spines and pencil-like branches, and the spiny flowers and fruits.

consisting of a multitude of small cylindrical branches, about one-fourth of an inch in diameter, covered with diamond-shaped plates from which project, here and there, solitary spines 1½ to 2 inches long (fig. 7). A papery sheath, like the scabbard of a sword, encloses each spine, and this may easily be pulled off. Although most plants are densely spiny, some forms occur with few or no spines. The plant is not very succulent; after the first season's growth, the branches become woody.

The flowers are exceedingly variable in color, from greenish through yellow, reddish, and brown (pl.1,a). They commonly appear during the midsummer desert heat of June and July, although flowering plants have been observed as early as April. The dry, spiny fruits have been likened to sand burrs.

Opuntia ramosissima is a plant of the desert floor and of alluvial washes generally below 3,000 feet. It is abundant throughout the southern Mojave Desert, the Colorado Desert, and the Borrego Valley. Some of the finest stands are east of Desert Center on Highway 10. In that area the plants become very large and bushy, even arborescent, and up to 6 feet tall. Some places support almost pure growths of this species as a unique desert shrubland.

In the area west of Lucerne Valley occurs the variety *denudata*, in which the long central spines are sparse or nearly absent.

Jumping Cholla; Teddy Bear Cactus
(*Opuntia bigelovii*)

Many an unwary easterner has seen this glistening plant as he enters California through the southeastern deserts, and has stopped to get a piece of what seems, from a distance, to be covered with soft, silvery bristles like a teddy bear. To his surprise the cactus jumps at him, or so he believes, and impales him on sharp spines. The spines are doubly wicked, for, being barbed, at the slightest touch they penetrate the flesh and are extracted with difficulty and pain. Pliers are usually required. The barbed spines, if broken off in the flesh, may, unless they fester out, travel through the body for months and emerge far from the place of entry. The joints, also, detach readily and litter the ground where the species grows; so one must be cautious not to brush against them with shoe or pant cuff.

Opuntia bigelovii is usually recognized easily by its treelike form and thick, densely spiny branches (pl. 1, *b*). The plant may reach a height of 6 to 8 feet, but is usually 3 to 4 feet tall, with silvery upper parts and dark, dingy trunk and old branch bases. The yellowish flowers with lavender streaks (pl. 1, *c*) appear during April, but are not conspicuous.

The Jumping Cholla is widely distributed through the southern Mojave Desert and Colorado Desert, where it grows on the lower slopes and alluvial fans of the desert hills usually below 3,000 feet. Good stands can be seen around Whitewater, near Palm Springs, and throughout much of the Anza-Borrego Desert State Park. An outstanding colony of this species occurs in the Joshua Tree National Monument's Cholla Cactus Garden.

Opuntia bigelovii has apparently produced at least two natural hybrids with other California chollas. In Mason Valley and Vallecito in San Diego County, a colony known as *O. × fosbergii* seems to be a hybrid with *O. echinocarpa* and to exhibit intermediate characters. A somewhat similar supposed hybrid with *O. acanthocarpa*, called *O. × munzii*, is known from Beal's Well Wash in the Chocolate Mountains of Imperial County.

Coast Cholla (*Opuntia prolifera*)

Along coastal hills and bluffs from Ventura to Baja California and on the Channel Islands one frequently

[18]

sees a small treelike cholla with abundant, persistent green fruits. This is *Opuntia prolifera,* so named for the fruits, which are proliferous and grow one upon another in series. It is easily recognized. Since its range is restricted to the coast and the islands, it never extends far enough inland to be confused with the desert species. In San Diego County, where it sometimes mingles with another coastal species, *O. serpentina,* it is distinguished by its erect, treelike habit. Plants may reach a height of 6 feet, but are usually 2 to 3 feet tall.

The flowers are rose red to purplish (pl. 2, *a*), appearing in spring, but too small to be conspicuous. The fruits are almost always sterile and usually bear more flowers at the next season, as if they were branches. This may continue for several years until the mass of persistent fruits, forming short, pendant chains, becomes so heavy as to break the bearing branch. As in *O. bigelovii,* the joints (fig. 5) are readily detached and often litter the ground, where many take root to produce new plants.

This species may be observed on the few remaining undeveloped chaparral hillslopes along Highway 101 in Orange and San Diego counties, such as those north of Laguna Beach and Newport Beach. It occurs on the nature trail in the Cabrillo National Monument.

Silver Cholla; Golden Cholla
(*Opuntia echinocarpa*)

This is the widest ranging, commonest, and most variable of the California chollas, extending from Mono County to Mexico and eastward into Utah and Arizona. In areas of its best development it is characterized by an erect habit, growing 3 to 4 feet tall, with a distinct trunk and a dense crown of cylindrical branches whose joints are mostly 4 to 6 inches long and in part readily detached. The young branches are exceedingly spiny; the spines usually have silvery or yellow sheaths that give sparkle and color to the plant (pl. 1, *f*). Unlike its near relative, *Opuntia acanthocarpa*, this species has short tubercles only once or twice as long as broad, and a denser spination.

The flowers, although variable, are generally greenish-yellow with a reddish midrib, clustered in groups of four or more at the ends of branches. "Echinocarpa" comes from the Latin meaning "prickly fruit." The species has a dry rather than fleshy fruit, with many spines (fig. 8), but few of the fruits mature to bear seeds.

The plant can be observed on virtually any trip to California desert areas, for it occupies desert floors, mesas, foothills, and slopes from sea level to nearly 6,000 feet from southern Mono County through Inyo County, eastern Kern County, northern Los Angeles County, and throughout the Mojave and Colorado deserts. Size, density of spines, and color of sheath vary widely, but there is no satisfactory basis for distinguishing more than one species through much of this range. In eastern Riverside and Imperial counties, however, *O. echinocarpa* mingles with *O. acanthocarpa*, but is distinguished by its shorter tubercles, shorter branches, and more erect habit. The northern Mojave Desert forms tend to be short-arborescent. Around the western upper edges of the Colorado Desert and the Borrego Valley the plants are usually more spreading, branched from the base, without a definite trunk. These bushy forms, of various spine colors, are common east of Jacumba on Highway 80.

Buckhorn Cholla; Cane Cactus
(*Opuntia acanthocarpa*)

Just as "echino" comes from the Latin and means "prickly," "acantho," from the Greek, means the same. We have two California chollas with spiny fruits

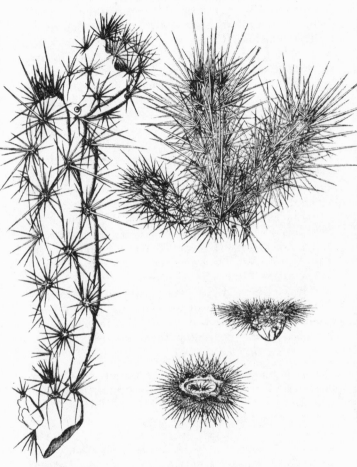

Fig. 8. *Opuntia acanthocarpa*, showing elongate tubercles of a well-watered specimen, a spiny dehydrated specimen, and spiny fruits much like those of *O. echinocarpa*.

(carpa). *Opuntia acanthocarpa* is generally more eastern and southern in distribution than *O. echinocarpa*, and is more characteristic of Arizona, although it extends well into our Mojave and Colorado deserts.

The Buckhorn Cholla is usually more bushy and outreaching than the Silver Cholla, and tends to have a much shorter or less-defined trunk when well developed. The branches are usually longer-jointed (6 to 18 inches) and the tubercules much elongated, three to four times as long as wide (fig. 8). Because of variations in both of these characters, however, distinctions are not always easy (pl. 1, *e*).

Opuntia acanthocarpa begins to mingle with *O. echinocarpa* east of Twentynine Palms and in the Chocolate Mountains east of the Salton Sea. In the vicinity of the Colorado River, however, *O. echinocarpa* fades out and *O. acanthocarpa* takes over as the only bushy cholla along our southeastern borders. It may be seen along Highway 95 north of Blythe, in the Palo Verde Mountains, and near Laguna Dam.

The name Cane Cactus refers to the use of the woody skeletons of the plant in the manufacture of canes and novelty woodcraft. The wood is hard and takes a good polish. The open lattice formed by the vascular system provides aesthetic appeal.

Valley Cholla (*Opuntia parryi*)

This is the most characteristic cylindrical *Opuntia* of the interior valleys and scrub-covered flats south and west of the deserts in southern California. It occurs more or less commonly from Cuyama Valley in Santa Barbara County, to Castaic in Los Angeles County, to Cajon Pass in San Bernardino County, and to the western edges of the Colorado and Borrego deserts. In some of our coastal areas it mingles with *O. prolifera,* and, toward the desert, with *O. echinocarpa,* but throughout much of its range west of the deserts it is the only cholla.

Opuntia parryi usually has relatively few rather long, canelike branches from the base, reaching 4 to 6 feet or more in height (pl. 2, *b*). Some plants, however, are very compactly branched and short. Others may show a densely branched arborescent habit. The joints tend to be long, for one year's growth often follows another without interruption as a joint. The branches are about an inch thick, and young ones detach easily. Since the plants tend to be rather lightly spined, the prominent tubercles show very clearly (fig. 9). The spines, brownish and inconspicuous compared with those of *O. echinocarpa,* lose their sheaths after the first season.

Fig. 9. *Opuntia parryi,* showing a young branch with prominent elongate tubercles, light spination, and fairly persistent leaves.

The inconspicuous flowers are greenish or yellowish within but reddish without. Few fruits are fertile and, unlike *O. prolifera*, these drop off the plant and do not persist to produce more flowers.

The taller forms of this species may be observed along the Santa Ana River west of Riverside, along Highway 395 in Cajon Pass, and in Castaic Canyon on Highway 99. A veritable *O. parryi* forest of small arborescent plants 3 to 5 feet tall occurs on the north side of Highway 10 just east of Cabazon. An interesting, broadly bushy, low-growing form may be seen at Banner, near Julian, on Highway 78.

Snake Cholla (*Opuntia serpentina*)

Although the Snake Cholla was one of the first cacti discovered in California, it has had a curious and confused history. First collected at San Diego (then part of Mexico) in 1838, it was provisionally named *Cereus californicus*. Later it was described in 1852 and renamed *Opuntia serpentina*, by which we still know it. For many years its rarity, local coastal distribution, and variable habit were not understood, and it was confused with other plants. During the early part of this century, collectors were unable to find it, and for some years it was considered extinct. In 1933 it was rediscovered near San Diego and brought into cultivation. We now know it as a species found in California only at Point Loma and near Chula Vista and San Ysidro, but extending southward along the Baja California coast.

Opuntia serpentina is a small cholla, usually of spreading or even prostrate habit. Some plants, however, are more or less erect. It often grows in company with *O. prolifera*, with which it apparently hybridizes to produce confusing intermediates, but plants of the two species ordinarily show very contrasting charactereristics when observed together (pl. 5, *e*).

The yellowish-green flowers are produced during April and May in a cluster near the ends of the growing branches. The fruits are dry at maturity and contain large whitish seeds.

A good place to see this plant is on a gentle slope just below the lighthouse and nature trail at Point Loma in the Cabrillo National Monument, where an excellent comparison with *O. prolifera* can be made.

Devil's Cactus (*Opuntia parishii*)

At elevations of 3,000 to 4,000 feet in the Mojave Desert at the foot of alluvial fans and on north slopes of desert ranges, occasional mats of this low, spreading cactus are seen. The stems are short, produce roots along the undersides, and grow outward from the initial point to form broad clusters and mats up to 10 feet across. The stems are almost hidden under a dense armament of angled, flattened spines an inch or more long (fig. 10). Young spines are red or pinkish, but they fade to gray at maturity, blending remarkably with the short, dry desert grass in natural camouflage. The yellow flowers appear in May and June. The fruits, about 2 inches long, are spineless but completely covered with yellow bristles (pl. 2, *c*).

This plant can be observed a few miles south of Twentynine Palms on the mesa in the Joshua Tree National Monument, and occurs in scattered patches all the way north to Clark Mountain near Highway 15. Another good place is between Cima and Goffs in northeastern San Bernardino County.

The plant was first described in the Pacific Railroad Survey report in 1856, but its present name, honoring the laborious early trips through the Mojave Desert by the San Bernardino botanist Samuel Parish, dates from 1896. It is sometimes treated as a subspecies of a more widespread Arizona species, *O. stanlyi*.

In easternmost Imperial County occurs a much

Fig. 10. *Opuntia parishii,* showing two joints and flattened spines.

larger form of the Devil's Cactus, *Opuntia wrightiana,* with stems 4 to 8 inches long and 1 to 1½ inches in diameter (fig. 11). It is sometimes treated as a subspecies in the *O. stanlyi* complex comparable with *O. parishii.* The plant may be found on the flats southwest of Winterhaven, near Yuma.

Dwarf Cholla (*Opuntia pulchella*)

The Dwarf Cholla is one of a group of inconspicuous small chollas (sometimes known as *Micropuntia*) characterized by large tuberous underground stems and very short, clustered, aboveground stems only 1 to 4 inches high (fig. 12). The plants occur in areas in which cacti are unexpected and, being exceedingly small and inconspicuous in the grass, are seldom seen except when the relatively large purple flowers (1 to 1½ inches) are open. The range is from northern

Arizona and southwestern Utah across southern Nevada to the edge of California in Mono County in the vicinity of the White Mountains and probably the Walker River.

Fig. 11. *Opuntia wrightiana,* showing joints and bristle-covered fruit.

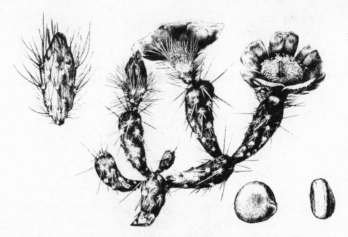

Fig. 12. *Opuntia pulchella*, showing part of a flowering plant, a spiny bud, and two seeds.

PLATYOPUNTIA: THE PRICKLY PEARS

The prickly pears are the most tolerant and widespread of all cacti and occur in the greatest number of species (more than 200). They comprise the one group that ranges in California from farthest north to farthest south. In their principal homeland, Mexico, they have been used since the ancient times of the Toltecs and Aztecs. The fruits and the tender young pads have long been common foods (tunas and nopales). The plants are widely cultivated for hedges. The juice is employed medicinally for burns, as a laxative, and in the treatment of diabetes. In California the prickly pear received great notoriety as a result of Luther Burbank's development of spineless cacti. In some countries, particularly Australia, introduced opuntias were once serious pests and, before controls were developed, spread over millions of acres.

The California prickly pears are the most difficult of our cacti to identify because of their great variation and extensive intergradation. Much of this is due to the ability of the natural species to hybridize with one another and with the two principal forms of cacti introduced from Mexico 200 years ago by the mission founders along El Camino Real.

Beaver Tail Cactus (*Opuntia basilaris*)
(Illustrated on front cover)

The Beaver Tail Cactus, a widespread *Opuntia* of our deserts and mountains, bears some of the loveliest flowers of any of our native plants. These cacti occur in a diversity of habitats and show a wide range of forms.

Typical *Opuntia basilaris* is a low-growing plant consisting of several flat, obovate pads, 5 to 10 inches long, arising from a common base. The pads are greenish to purplish, often transversely wrinkled, and apparently spineless (fig. 13). They suggest the shape of a beaver's tail. Although the areoles bear no obvious spines, they are filled with packs of glochids which can cause great misery if they get on one's clothing and then into the skin. From March to June in various parts of our deserts this plant produces magnificent cluster of rose- to orchid-colored flowers up to 3 inches across. The fruits are dry when ripe and contain whitish seeds. This is one of the succulent plants widely used in ancient times by the desert Indians, such as the Panamint tribe. All parts were used for food: pads, flower buds, young fruits, and seeds.

Opuntia basilaris in its typical form may be found throughout much of the Mojave, Colorado, and Borrego deserts from nearly 6,000 feet to about sea level. It may be seen upon entering the desert by highways 10, 15, 74, 80, and 78, and throughout much of the

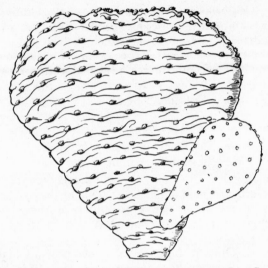

Fig. 13. *Opuntia basilaris.* A young pad and an old, wrinkled pad.

Joshua Tree National Monument and the Anza-Borrego Desert State Park.

A number of interesting forms of *O. basilaris* occur other than the typical one. In Kern County east of Bakersfield is the variety *treleasii,* best seen on either side of Walker Pass. It is marked by the presence of spines in the areoles in addition to the glochids. Along the east slope of the Sierra Nevada in Inyo and Mono counties at elevations up to 9,000 feet (such as the middle slopes of Mount Whitney), is a dwarfish, pink-flowered form, sometimes with white flowers, known as variety *whitneyana.* On desert slopes of the San Gabriel and San Bernardino mountains may be found the variety *brachyclada,* with very narrow, short, thick, and fingerlike pads. In the interior valleys of coastal drainage in southern California, especially from San Bernardino to Claremont, occurs a form in which the pads are branched in upper parts instead of only at the base. This is the variety *ramosa* (pl. 5, *d*). Each of these major variants has been treated by some students of cacti as a separate species. They do tend to maintain their distinctive characteristics in cultivation.

Opuntia basilaris var. *brachyclada* has been called the Snow Flower Cactus, for it comes into brilliant flower soon after melting of the snow that covers the plant in winter. It grows under piñon pines and mountain shrubs at elevations of 4,000 to 7,500 feet around Wrightwood and in Swartout Valley.

Old Man Prickly Pear; Grizzly Bear Cactus
(*Opuntia erinacea*)

Opuntia erinacea has a low-growing, clumping habit similar to that of *O. basilaris,* but the pads are covered with grayish, whitish, or even blackish spines of varying length. In the form known as *O. erinacea* var. *ursina,* the white spines are so long and soft as to cover the plant with a kind of white hair (pl. 2, *d*). These hairy plants are popular as novelty specimens in gardens, and wild populations are rapidly being reduced by plant hunters. At the other extreme is the variety *xanthostema* in which the spines are sparse, short, and mostly absent from the lower half of the joints. The flowers of these diverse forms of *O. erinacea* are prevailingly yellow, but vary to pink and reddish. The fruits are dry and short-spiny.

Typical *O. erinacea,* which has abundant rigid spines 1 to 2 inches or more long (pl. 2, *e*), is a plant of moderate elevations (2,500 to 8,000 feet) in the western Mojave Desert from the San Bernardino Mountains through Inyo County to Mono County. A fine stand occurs in Wild Rose Canyon near the entrance to Death Valley. A far southern colony lives in the Santa Rosa Mountains of Riverside County.

The long-haired variety *ursina* occurs in the central and eastern Mojave Desert at elevations of 3,000 to 4,500 feet. It was discovered in 1894 by A. H. Alverson of San Bernardino, a cactus enthusiast who operated a prospector's supply outpost. When he learned from a desert gold seeker of the existence of a cactus with white hair a foot long, he organized a horse-and-wagon party to find it. The party suffered great hardships on the desert for lack of water, but found the plant in the Ord Mountains and introduced it to the horticultural world. It may be seen there today, where it is regenerating after suffering near-extinction at the hands of commercial collectors two decades ago.

The lightly spined variety *xanthostema* has a remarkable distribution for a cactus. It is a high-elevation form that survives heavy snow cover. It grows on desert slopes of the Sierra Nevada and the White Mountains as high as 11,000 feet. A visitor to Convict Lake in Mono County will find it on sandy exposures around the east end of the lake.

Golden Prickly Pear; Pancake Pear
(*Opuntia chlorotica*)
(Illustrated on front cover)

Opuntia chlorotica is one of our few distinctive large prickly pears. A striking plant when well developed, it has bright yellow spines and a prominent treelike habit with definite trunk often covered with a thatch of long spines. The yellow flowers show little contrast with the spines, but the fruits are bright red or purplish. The plant reaches a height of 6 or more feet, and has such well-rounded pads that it is referred to as Pancake Pear (pl. 2, *f*; fig. 14).

Although it is prominent and easily recognized, the plant is not often seen in California, for its habitats here are scattered and mostly not readily accessible.

a. *Opuntia ramosissima*

b. *Opuntia bigelovii*

c. *Opuntia bigelovii*

d. *Opuntia acanthocarpa*

e. *Opuntia acanthocarpa*

f. *Opuntia echinocarpa*

PLATE 1

a. Opuntia prolifera   *b. Opuntia parryi*

c. Opuntia parishii   *d. Opuntia ursina*

e. Opuntia erinacea   *f. Opuntia chlorotica*

PLATE 2

a. Opuntia ficus-indica *b. Opuntia megacantha*

c. Opuntia oricola (l.); *d. Opuntia littoralis*
Opuntia littoralis (r.)

e, f. Opuntia vaseyi (red); *Opuntia covillei* (yellow)

PLATE 3

a. Opuntia piercei   *b. Opuntia piercei*

c. Opuntia occidentalis   *d. Opuntia occidentalis*

f. Opuntia megacarpa

e. Opuntia oricola

PLATE 4

a. Bergerocactus emoryi   *b. Echinocereus engelmannii*

c. Ferocactus covillei   *d. Opuntia basilaris* var. *ramosa*

e. Opuntia prolifera (erect); *Opuntia serpentina* (low).

PLATE 5

a. Carnegiea gigantea   *b. Carnegiea gigantea*

c. Echinocereus boyce-thompsonii   *d. Echinomastus johnsonii*

e. Echinocereus engelmannii   *f. Echinocereus mojavensis*

PLATE 6

a. Echinocactus polycephalus   *b. Echinocactus polycephalus*

c. Ferocactus acanthodes   *d. Ferocactus acanthodes*

e. Ferocactus viridescens   *f. Sclerocactus polyancistrus*

PLATE 7

a. Coryphantha deserti   *b. Coryphantha alversonii*

c. Coryphantha alversonii   *d. Coryphantha arizonica*

e. Mammillaria dioica   *f. Phellosperma tetrancistra*

PLATE 8

Fig. 14. *Opuntia chlorotica,* showing a single round pad.

Abundant growths occur in Arizona, New Mexico, and Sonora, Mexico. Perhaps the best place to see *O. chlorotica* conveniently is in Sentenac Canyon on Highway 78 below Julian, where many specimens stand on the steep south walls of the gorge below Scissors Crossing. On Highway 80 it occurs 3.3 miles east of Pine Valley and along the Mexican boundary fence 3 miles east of Jacumba. It is more widely distributed throughout the eastern half of San Bernardino County, where it grows in mountainous areas and on desert plateaus at about 4,000 feet. Some large plants occur in the Joshua Tree National Monument, and fine stands may be seen between Goffs and Cima in the Providence Mountains region.

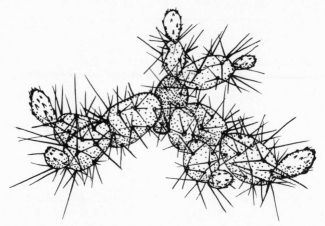

Fig. 15. *Opuntia fragilis.* Habit of part of a plant.

Pigmy Tuna (*Opuntia fragilis*)

This small prickly pear is one of the few cacti adapted to life in the severe climate of interior continental America. It grows as far north as Manitoba, Canada, and survives heavy winter snows and temperatures as low as 50° below zero. It is characteristic of the Great Plains, forming low, spreading clusters and mounds 1 to 4 feet in diameter, but mostly hidden in grass. It has been a troublesome weed in grazing country because of the small, thick, spiny joints which become detached at the slightest touch and fasten into the flesh of the nose and lips of range animals (fig. 15).

The plant is widely distributed in arid parts of the Northwest between southern British Columbia and northern California. We find it in Siskiyou County in dry places in the juniper country. It flowers in May and June, but the pale yellow flowers are sparse and seldom seen.

[34]

Indian Fig (*Opuntia ficus-indica*)

This large, shrubby to treelike, nearly spineless cactus probably had its origins in prehistoric times in tropical America. Most likely it was developed in the Mexican region and was already widely cultivated, mainly for its fruits (fig. 16), when the Spaniards arrived. It was soon transplanted to Europe, north Africa, and other regions where it became naturalized. Large plantations were established in the Mediterranean area. One of the most important agricultural crops of Sicily has long been *Opuntia* fruits, of which some 18,000 pounds per acre can be harvested (pl. 3, *a*).

The Indian Fig, introduced into southern California from Mexico as one of the mission cacti, has spread with *O. megacantha* throughout much of the cismontane part of the state. Similarity with the spiny *O.*

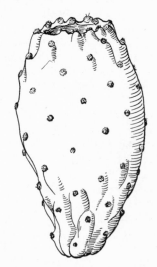

Fig. 16.   *Opuntia ficus-indica*, fruit.

megacantha and occasional reversions of the spineless form to spiny ones strongly suggest the origin of this plant from *O. megacantha*. Both plants hybridize freely with each other and with several of the native California prickly pears.

Large treelike examples of this plant with smooth, elongate, nearly spineless pads may be seen near each of the old California missions along El Camino Real from San Diego to San Francisco Bay. A commercial row-planting occurs on the east side of Highway 101 about 3 miles south of Coyote, near San Jose.

Mission Cactus (*Opuntia megacantha*)

From the Mission Cactus the best varieties of edible fruits are obtained. It is similar to *Opuntia ficus-indica*, but has more rounded pads and fairly abundant coarse spines. It forms similar large treelike plants which in age develop heavy trunks. The flowers, yellow to yellow-orange, are producd mostly in May and June. The large yellowish to reddish fruits (pl. 3, *b*) mature in November and December. They are spineless, but have many glochids which must be brushed off carefully before the fruit is handled.

Opuntia megacantha came into California two hundred years ago at Mission San Diego de Alcalá. Pieces subsequently planted along the old Mexican trails hybridized widely with several species of prickly pears. The resulting hybrid swarm of variations has made it increasingly difficult to identify the several natural species from Santa Barbara to San Bernardino and San Diego, whose natural distributions and characteristics are unknown to us. Within a single prickly pear thicket one may find plants showing a wide range of characters linking them in varying degrees to one or several of the named species treated below.

Like the Indian Fig, the Mission Cactus may be seen in clearly recognizable typical form around the Spanish mission communities along El Camino Real, but there are numerous confusing intergrades as well. One of the largest stands occurs at La Purisima Mission near Lompoc.

An important unnamed hybrid form, probably involving *O. covillei*, occurs from Claremont to Murrieta and east of the Santa Ana Mountains. It is a shorter, more shrubby form than typical *O. megacantha* and has weak spination. The flowers are larger and more rotate. The fruits are reddish-purple, oblong and basally tapered.

Short Coastal Prickly Pear (*Opuntia littoralis*)

Opuntia littoralis has long been considered the principal prickly pear along coastal southern California from Santa Barbara to San Diego and southward, usually within about 5 miles of the coast, but occasionally inland at low elevations and also on the Channel Islands. Recently it has been determined that more than one species is involved throughout this range. Besides *O. littoralis* and the recently described *O. oricola*, other kinds of fleshy-fruited prickly pears grow in relatively restricted areas along the southern California coast, but since these remain unnamed, we shall not consider them here.

Opuntia littoralis is a more spreading plant than *O. oricola*, seldom erect, and usually less than 4 feet tall. Besides their habit of growth, the two species exhibit several other conspicuous differences. The pads of *O. littoralis* are more oblong-elliptical, and the spines are usually straight (pl. 3, *c*). The color of unweathered spines is bone white rather than clear, translucent yellowish. The fruits have an obpyriform rather than globular shape (pl. 3, *d*). The morphological characters of *O. littoralis* are somewhat more varied than those of the clearly defined *O. oricola*.

Both species may be met within nearly every coastal and insular prickly pear colony. Some good places to see and compare them are along Highway 101 entering the Conejo Mountains east of Camarillo, on the sea cliffs near Malibu Beach, along the seaward Palos Verdes Hills, on the coast north of Laguna Beach at Irvine Cove, at Dana Point Cove off Green Lantern Street, and in the Cabrillo National Monument at San Diego.

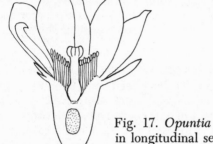

Fig. 17. *Opuntia oricola,* flower in longitudinal section.

Tall Coast Prickly Pear (*Opuntia oricola*)

This newly described plant (1964) has long been confused with *Opuntia littoralis,* which has virtually the same range. When one learns the distinctions between the two, however, he can recognize each from a distance. *Opuntia oricola* is usually of erect rather than spreading habit; mature plants are often 6 feet or more tall. The pads are almost circular in outline rather than oblong-elliptical as in *O. littoralis.* Rather than bone white, the spines are a clear, translucent yellow in unweathered condition. Flowers are yellow as in *O. littoralis* (fig. 17). The fruits tend to be globular rather than elongate, and lack the narrowed base of *O. littoralis.* Although some of the spines are straight, and occasionally all may be nearly straight, the heavier spines are often characterized by a prominent downward curvature (pls. 3, *c,* 4, *e*).

These large plants can usually be spotted in colonies of coastal prickly pears by their round pads. Look for them in *Opuntia* thickets in the coastal sage vegetation all the way from San Diego to Santa Barbara and a few miles inland. Besides the several near-coastal localities mentioned under *O. littoralis*, a fine stand occurs on north Euclid Avenue in Fullerton. A few large specimens may be seen along Foothill Road near the Santa Barbara Botanic Garden, growing with *O. megacantha*.

Another coastal and near-coastal plant ranging from central Orange County to near San Diego and inland about 20 miles is an undescribed form showing some characteristics of *O. littoralis*, *O. occidentalis*, and *O. megacantha*. The pads are large, with widely spaced areoles, long yellow to yellow-brown spines, large rotate flowers, and large and persistent leaves.

Western Prickly Pear (*Opuntia occidentalis*)

There is much confusion over just what *Opuntia occidentalis* really is, although the name is widely used in floras and, indeed, various other plants are assigned to it as varieties or subspecies. The plant generally known under this name occupies a territory throughout most of Orange County and inland to the foothills of the San Gabriel Mountains. We recognize it as a large bushy plant reaching about 6 feet in height. It bears moderately heavy brown spines, with lighter golden tips, 1 to 1½ inches long and tending to be deflexed. A distinctive character is the long awl-shaped leaf on young pads, sometimes longer than half an inch. The flowers are yellowish to cream. The ovary is markedly tuberculate and has persistent leaves. The style is bulbous. Fruits are red to somewhat maroon and moderately large, about 2½ by 1¾ inches (pl. 4, c).

These plants may be found associated with *Opuntia vaseyi* and *O. covillei* in inland areas, and with *O.*

littoralis and *O. oricola* nearer the coast. They show evidence of being a hybrid between the Mission Cactus and *Opuntia vaseyi*.

Localities in which to observe characteristic plants of *O. occidentalis* are in the vicinity of Fullerton, especially at Yorba Linda and Placentia.

Salmon-flowered Prickly Pear (*Opuntia vaseyi*)

Opuntia vaseyi is a low-growing plant only 1 to 1½ feet tall and spreading to 8 to 10 feet, but with brown, golden-tipped spines similar to those of the more erect *O. occidentalis*. The flowers are distinctive in being deep salmon-colored, for this is the only one of our larger spiny prickly pears with such flowers (pl. 3, *e*).

The range is restricted to the inland valleys from about Buena Park north to San Dimas, east to Banning, and south to Hemet. There are no known coastal localities.

Opuntia vaseyi has been treated in some floras as a variety of *O. occidentalis,* but it is evidently an ancestral California type not modified by hybridization. It shows some vegetative variation in the direction of *O. piercei,* but not in flower color.

Good places to see this plant are along the foothills of the San Gabriel Mountains by State Highway 30 northeast of Upland.

Coville's Prickly Pear (*Opuntia covillei*)

Opuntia covillei is another variable prickly pear whose specific limits can scarcely be defined and whose identification cannot always clearly be made. It is a low-growing plant similar in habit to *O. vaseyi,* but with lemon-yellow flowers tinged with red on the outer perianth segments (pl. 3, *e*). Some plants may be bushy and up to 3 feet tall. The pads are more variable in shape than in *O. vaseyi,* and the spines, which are commonly twisted, are typically restricted to the upper half of the pad. The fruits are a dull purplish red.

Opuntia covillei represents a major segment of the hybrid swarm of prickly pears from the interior valleys of southern California. Some characters suggest relationship with the Mission Cactus and with *O. megacarpa*. Other characters suggest partial derivation, together with *O. vaseyi* and *O. piercei* of this same complex, from the widespread, more eastern *O. phaeacantha* common in Arizona. *Opuntia covillei* has been treated as a variety of *O. phaeacantha* and also as a variety of *O. occidentalis*.

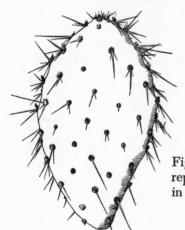

Fig. 18. An *Opuntia* pad representing one form within the *O. covillei* complex.

This variable assemblage now occupies a region encompassing Orange County and extending to the foothills of the San Gabriel and San Bernardino mountains. Toward the coast the distinction from *O. littoralis* becomes confused as the spination spreads over the entire pads.

Perhaps the most representative forms of this plant may be seen along State Highway 30 northeast of Upland, where it contrasts with the salmon-flowered *O. vaseyi* (pl. 3, *e*). It is part of the big hybrid mass of prickly pears conspicuous along the San Bernardino freeway just west of Pomona near the fairgrounds.

Banning Prickly Pear (*Opuntia megacarpa*)

Opuntia megacarpa, originally described from specimens collected at Banning, is distributed on dry mountain slopes around the western and southern edges of our deserts. The species shows relationship with two more easterly species in Arizona: *O. phaeacantha* and *O. engelmannii*. It has large pads and the plants are erect but short, not as decumbent as *O. piercei*, which often grows in the same area and with which it seems to merge and hybridize in San Diego County (pl. 4, *f*). The white and yellow spines, 2 inches or more long, tend to be twisted and not much downwardly deflected. They are rather uniformly distributed over the stem joints, whereas those of *O. piercei* are usually confined to the upper half. Glochids are conspicuous. The fruits are not necessarily or especially large, despite the name.

The range may be outlined as from Riverside and the east side of the Santa Ana Mountains, to the north side of Palomar Mountain, northeast to the desert slopes of the Santa Rosa and San Jacinto mountains, to the southern desert edges of the San Bernardino Mountains. Along the mountain slopes bordering the Anza-Borrego Desert *O. megacarpa* merges with *O. piercei*, and evident hybrid forms may be encountered.

Typical plants may be observed around Banning, and upgrade toward Redlands. A good stand grows in the vicinity of Lake Mathews.

Pierce's Prostrate Prickly Pear (*Opuntia piercei*)

Another plant related to the Arizona *Opuntia phaea-*

cantha, and originally described as a variety of it, is *O. piercei* from our desert mountain slopes at 3,000 to 7,000 feet. These remarkably prostrate plants form "creeping clumps" in which the joints root down successively at one end as they grow out one on another, and die back at the other end. The spines are 2 to 3 inches long and usually single from each areole in the upper half of the nearly circular pads. The flowers are yellow and the fruits red to dull purplish and slender (pl. 4, *a*).

This plant has a montane range on the desert sides of the San Gabriel, San Bernardino, Santa Rosa, and Laguna mountains. It occurs in areas receiving rather heavy winter snow. Some good places to observe *O. piercei* are above Baldwin Lake in the San Bernardino Mountains, at Warner's Hot Springs in San Diego County, along Highway 79 in the Cuyamaca Mountains, and along Highway 94 just east of Jacumba.

Mojave Desert Prickly Pear (*Opuntia mojavensis*)

The large-padded prickly pears of the California deserts have not been studied adequately, and we do not have a clear understanding of the relationship of

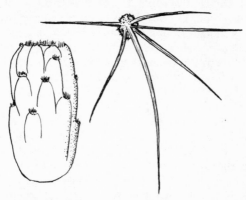

Fig. 19. *Opuntia mojavensis.* A young, spineless fruit and a spine cluster removed from a pad.

some of our forms to those eastward into Arizona and Nevada. *Opuntia mojavensis* evidently is closely related to *O. phaeacantha* and *O. engelmannii* in Arizona. It was described from the Providence Mountains area and is presently known from the eastern Mojave Desert north to the Clark Mountains. Some of the desert prickly pears in the Anza-Borrego Desert area seem closely related to *O. mojavensis* and to *O. engelmannii,* but have not been sufficiently investigated.

Opuntia mojavensis is a primarily prostrate plant in which the secondary pads are erect, but the whole plant is only about 1½ feet high. The joints are large (8 to 12 inches) and bear yellowish-brown, porrect spines up to 2½ inches long (fig. 19). The flowers are pale yellow to orange. The fruits are spineless, slender, and narrow at the base when mature.

Published localities for *O. mojavensis* include the vicinity of the Bonanza King mine in the Providence Mountains and the region adjoining Highway 95 on the California side of the Nevada state boundary.

Giant Cactus; Saguaro (*Carnegiea gigantea*)

So abundant and prevalent throughout Arizona is this magnificent succulent that it is often called the Arizona Giant Cactus. Indeed, near Tucson the Saguaro National Monument has been set up exclusively for it. Nevertheless, this plant occurs also in California, although not extensively or in large numbers (pl. 6, *a*). A few scattered specimens are found near the Colorado River from the Palo Verde Mountains southward toward Laguna Dam, near which a fairly large grove occurs. Another large stand is in the Whipple Mountains near the Parker Dam and reservoir. Thirty years ago, before Parker Lake was formed, it was known that many of the giant cacti would be flooded out by rising water, and permits were issued to cactus enthusiasts who wanted to transplant them. The writer, then in high school, was one of these, and it was to my extraordinary delight that my father agreed to help me bring one home as the biggest cactus in town. It was a 22-foot giant with two limbs, and required considerable engineering to get it home to Long Beach and plant it in the back yard. There it lived and flowered for many years before it finally succumbed to rot.

The saguaro is the northernmost of the giant columnar cacti of which a number of species and genera occur in Mexico and a few in South America. This species probably should be treated under one of the Mexican genera, but it has long honored Andrew Carnegie, the benefactor of Britton and Rose, who monographed the Cactaceae early in this century and dedicated the largest American cactus to him.

The giant cactus for centuries served the Indians of the Southwest with food, fuel, and building material. The season of ripe fruits brought whole tribal populations into the cactus forest for feasting and the preparation of dried fruits for winter use. One frugal tribe of the desert even saved the seeds from their own feces to be ground up and eaten a second time.

The huge fleshy stem is supported by a woody cylinder consisting of a ring of anastomosing poles of great strength. This strong internal skeleton accounts for the size of these plants, which may reach 60 feet. Flowering is in May and June (pl. 6, *b*).

Velvet Cactus (*Bergerocactus emoryi*)

In 1850 the United States and Mexican Boundary Survey party discovered this plant where the first international boundary marker was installed south of Imperial Beach in San Diego County. It still may be found there, although elsewhere in southern California *Bergerocactus* has largely been exterminated by our urban sprawl along the coast. As late as 1930 it could still be found at Oceanside and San Clemente, but only a few patches now remain around San Diego.

The best one is protected by the Cabrillo National Monument and is marked on its nature trail just below the lighthouse. It can be seen there in its characteristic habit, producing pale yellow flowers in spring, and fruits in late summer. The globular, spiny red fruits are peculiar in the manner in which they split open at maturity and allow the red pulp and black seeds to ooze out.

Bergerocactus is a seacoast plant that extends far south into Baja California. It is abundant on San Clemente Island and occurs to some extent on Santa Catalina. It forms thickets of erect or sprawling plants, 2 to 3 feet long or high, which multiply by sending out branches from below the surface of the ground. New stems have bright yellow spines which fade and darken with age (pl. 5, *a*).

This plant is often treated in western floras as *Cereus emoryi*. A number of characteristics make it unique, however, and when segregated from *Cereus* it remains the only member of this genus named for the German botanist Alwin Berger. In Baja California it is known to form natural hybrids with the large candelabra cactus (*Myrtillocactus*) and with the giant cardon (*Pachycereus*). The results are some very rare and peculiar cacti that are known only from one or a very few specimens (*Myrtgerocactus* and *Pachgerocereus*).

Hedgehog Cactus; Strawberry Cactus
(*Echinocereus engelmannii*)

The brilliantly colored magenta to purplish flowers of the Hedgehog Cactus make it a popular subject for illustrations of desert wildflowers (pl. 5, *b*). Moreover, the species is one of the most abundant of the freely flowering kinds in arid regions close to population centers in southern California. It is an exceedingly spiny plant made up of several to many elongate heads loosely arranged in a clump, the 2-to-3-inch spines interlacing the spaces between (pl. 6, *e*).

The flowers of hedgehog cacti are fairly long-lasting, opening each of several mornings and closing at night. They vary in color, but tend to have bluish tones from pigment mixtures unlike those of *E. mojavensis,* in which only red pigment occurs. The common name Strawberry Cactus refers to the succulent, edible red fruits which drop their spines when ripe.

Echinocereus engelmannii has a wide range in California, from nearly sea level in the Colorado Desert to elevations of 7,000 feet on dry slopes. It extends north through the Mojave Desert to the White Mountains and on into Arizona. The species may be observed throughout much of the Joshua Tree National Monument and the Anza-Borrego Desert State Park. One of the most abundant stands is on the hills along Highway 80 just east of Jacumba, where the plants are spaced only a few feet apart.

Some authors recognize *E. munzii* as a separate species; this plant, which is at least very closely related, occurs in mountain areas in Riverside, San Bernardino, and San Diego counties at the lower edge of the yellow-pine forest and into the piñon-juniper woodlands. It tends to form very compact clumps of numerous stems. It may be seen above Baldwin Lake on the desert slopes of the San Bernardino Mountains.

Mound Cactus; Mojave Hedgehog Cactus
(*Echinocereus mojavensis*)

Adult plants of this species form massive hemispherical mounds several feet in diameter, composed of enormous numbers of densely-packed spiny stems radiating from a common center. Plants with 500 to 800 of these heads have been reported. The spines, white or gray, are 1 to 2 inches long. The deep scarlet color of the flowers is striking in contrast to the pale spines (pl. 6, *f*). They appear around Easter time.

[47]

This remarkable plant was discovered more than a hundred years ago as a result of explorations for the route of the Pacific Railway. It was first illustrated in 1856. We now know it to occur widely but not very abundantly throughout mountain ranges of the Mojave Desert from the desert slopes of the San Bernardino range northeast to Clark Mountain and on through Death Valley National Monument to the White Mountains. It may be found in association with Creosote Bush, Joshua Tree, or Piñon Pine and Juniper, but it is a plant of rocky slopes at elevations of 3,000 to 7,000 feet and not of desert floors. It may be seen in the Joshua Tree National Monument associated with *Opuntia parishii,* a few miles south of Twentynine Palms on the mesa at Lost Horse Well, and around Mitchell's Caverns in the Providence Mountains.

Some workers consider this plant a variant of *Echinocereus triglochidiatus,* a species of broad distribution and great variability eastward through Arizona, New Mexico, and Texas. However, in California it is markedly distinct from any other cactus, particularly when in flower.

Boyce Thompson Hedgehog Cactus
(*Echinocereus boyce-thompsonii*)

The Clark Mountain area north of Valley Wells in far northeastern San Bernardino County is a California outpost for this plant characteristically found in central Arizona. It is generally treated as a subspecific variant within the *Echinocereus fendleri* complex, which includes diverse plants through Arizona, New Mexico, and Sonora. This one resembles *E. engelmannii* superficially in its rather open clusters of several elongate fleshy stems, but is distinct in having only a single prominent, deflexed central spine from each areole. These long central spines are distinctly light-colored and contrast with the dark radials (pl. 6, *c*). The flowers, magenta to purplish, are 2 to 2¾ inches in diameter.

Desert Barrel Cactus (*Ferocactus acanthodes*)

This legendary plant is supposed to have saved many a desert traveler from death by thirst. To be sure, it has a succulent pulp from which life-sustaining though unpleasant moisture can be obtained by crushing or chewing the flesh, but it is not cool, clear liquid water. In recent decades this succulent flesh, not unlike watermelon rind, has been employed in making cactus candy and pickles, although the plants are now protected by law against such use.

The Desert Barrel Cactus is easy to recognize, but variations in size, shape, and color have led botanists in the past to see several species in the assemblage. The commonest form is heavy-bodied and short, usually less than 3 feet tall and a foot or more in diameter. It occurs on most rocky slopes leading to the Borrego and Colorado deserts (pl. 7, *c*). In southeasternmost Imperial County are some very tall forms that may exceed 8 feet. The spines are generally yellow or straw-colored, but some examples have bright red spines and others have gray or white spines. All these are now considered variants of the single species. The yellow flowers often present a colorful corona (pl. 7, *d*).

Most plants have solitary heads, but clusters of two or three are sometimes seen. These are usually separate plants growing close together, since the barrel cacti infrequently branch. Growth is very slow, and may occur only at long intervals. In fact, these plants, with their reserve water supply, can live and flower year after year sitting on a dry shelf in the sun.

Ferocactus acanthodes ranges through the Borrego and Colorado deserts and the middle and eastern Mojave Desert below 5,000 feet, and on into Arizona, Nevada, and Baja California. Good stands may be observed at Split Rock in the Joshua Tree National Monument, in the Devil's Playground area south of

Baker, in Sentenac Canyon below Julian, and on the Mountain Springs grade west of El Centro. A fine display occurs on the north side of Highway 10 just below Whitewater, near Palm Springs.

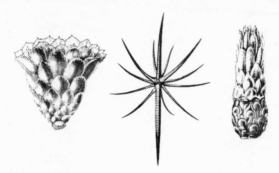

Fig. 20. *Ferocactus viridescens,* showing flower, fruit, and spine cluster.

Coast Barrel Cactus (*Ferocactus viridescens*)

This species of "fierce" cactus is so small and low that it scarcely suggests the barrel form of its near relative *Ferocactus acanthodes*. It is distinct, too, in habitat, for it is strictly a coastal species of San Diego County and northern Baja California, seldom occurring more than 20 miles from the shore. It lives in the chaparral north to about Escondido and is especially common in the Cabrillo National Monument at Point Loma, San Diego, where it can be observed conveniently on the nature trail. Some of the finest and largest plants occur on Otay Mesa a few miles southeast. The specimens usually form single heads, but clusters of several are not uncommon.

The name "viridescens" refers to the greenish flowers which appear in spring (fig. 20), followed by spineless yellow fruits (pl. 7, *e*), which contain quantities of black seeds easily removed at maturity. These were among the common food seeds of the San Diego Indians before Spanish grains were brought to California.

This is a good plant in which to observe protective armament, for the spination has developed remarkably complete protection against herbivores. The central spines are exceedingly strong and so symmetrically arranged as to fend off deer or rabbits from any direction. The radial spines form a protective mesh over the succulent ribs and are so securely fastened that they can scarcely be removed even by a pawing hoof (fig. 20).

Coville's Barrel Cactus (*Ferocactus covillei*)

Not long ago some amateur cactus hunters brought into my office a young specimen of a barrel cactus that they had never before found in California. Although juvenile, this plant seemed to have all the characters of *Ferocactus covillei*, particularly the single heavy, hooked central spine and the small number of strong radials. It was said to have come from a canyon along the Mexican boundary a few miles east of Jacumba in southwesternmost Imperial County. The known range of this species otherwise is about 200 miles farther east in Arizona (pl. 5, *c*).

Nigger Heads (*Echinocactus polycephalus*)

The old genus *Echinocactus* of nineteenth-century authors contains over a thousand names, and embraces a great diversity of cactus species of globular form. Britton and Rose, in volume 3 of their monograph on the Cactaceae in 1922, recognized a number of distinctive genera within the assemblage and restricted *Echinocactus* to a small group of barrel cacti with dense wool at the top of the plant. Some manuals, however, continue to use *Echinocactus* in the old inclusive sense.

[51]

Most species of *Echinocactus* are ponderous, single-headed giants from central Mexico, but, as the name indicates, *E. polycephalus* is a many-headed form. Plants with 10 to 20 heads are common, and an enormous specimen of 132 heads grew near Yermo until it was hacked to pieces by vandals (pl. 7, *a*).

Except for very young plants, this species is immediately distinguished from *Ferocactus acanthodes* by its multiheaded character. The yellow flowers are borne in the woolly crown. The fruits are densely woolly (fig. 21), dry at maturity, and open by a basal pore.

Echinocactus polycephalus is a plant of the most forbidding, hot, dry desert mountains, from northern Inyo County and the Panamints beside Death Valley to Randsburg and Victorville in the Mojave Desert, and on east into Arizona. A small outlying colony occurs in the Coyote Mountains of Imperial County. The species can be observed in characteristic habitat around Barstow and Calico Ghost Town off Highway 15. Some fine stands occur around Scotty's Castle in Death Valley.

Fig. 21.   *Echinocactus polycephalus*, fruit.

Pigmy Barrel Cactus (*Echinomastus johnsonii*)

This distinctive small barrel cactus is seldom seen in California on account of the remoteness of its habitat in the far northeastern Mojave Desert, north of the Kingston range in the east corner of Inyo County, and east of the Ivanpah Mountains. It is occasional there on dry rocky slopes and washes, a small, solitary barrel cactus 5 to 10 inches high. It consists of 18 to 20 spiral ribs fairly well marked into tubercles and provided with dense, coarse, nearly straight spines.

The plant generally appears in floras as *Echinocactus johnsonii* and has also been treated as a species of *Ferocactus*. Specialists in recent years have considered the small size, the low ribs with felted grooves, and the short-tubed flowers as characters of the genus *Echinomastus*, which includes similar species in Utah and Arizona.

The flowers appear in groups and protrude from between the spines at the apex (pl. 6, *d*). They are of variable color, from deep red and brownish to pink, salmon, apricot, and even white. In one Nevada form they are lemon yellow. They have the unusual capacity of opening and closing for as many as seven successive days.

This plant may be observed in sparse colonies in the hills in the vicinity of Shoshone along Highway 127 east of Death Valley and in the New York Mountains near Ivanpah.

Long-spined Fishhook Cactus
(*Sclerocactus polyancistrus*)

The magnificent spiny beauty of this colorful succulent is leading to its extinction in all desert areas frequented by man. The plant is solitary, unbranched, 8 to 12 inches tall, and covered with long white and maroon spines of which the longest colored ones are strongly hooked (fig. 22). So rare and peculiar is the plant that anyone finding it in the desert is inclined

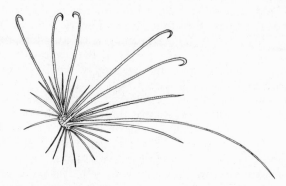

Fig. 22. *Sclerocactus polyancistrus* spine cluster.

to dig it up and take it home. This is the end of the cactus, for *Sclerocactus* does not live well or long in cultivation, often because of rot that forms in the passages made by a boring grub in the fleshy tissues of this species. In nature the plant seals off the wounds and survives, but not in captivity.

The flowers are magenta, from the apex (pl. 7, *f*), and the fruits are smooth and red.

Several widely scattered areas of the Mojave Desert in which this rare plant grows have been searched so thoroughly by cactus hunters that few specimens may now be found within easy access of roads. Nevertheless, a good desert hiker may luckily find this prized species in the Roaring Ridge area of Red Rock Canyon, or between Adelanto, Oro Grande, and Helendale west of Highway 15. (These are also the homelands of the desert tortoise.) Very large specimens occur in the Opal Mountain area north of Barstow.

Desert Pincushion Cactus *(Coryphantha deserti)*

The California coryphanthas comprise a group of small, single- or multi-headed cacti which can be distinguished from our mammillarias by the straight spines and by a groove on the upper side of the tubercles. We have three kinds, of which this was the first described by Englemann in 1880 from Ivanpah, then an outpost of the Union Pacific Railroad line in the eastern Mojave Desert. Some workers prefer to treat the three plants as subspecies under *Coryphantha* (or *Mammillaria*) *vivipara*, a widespread species through Arizona, New Mexico, and Sonora, Mexico. The purposes of the present handbook, however, call for the use of different specific names as a matter of convenience.

Coryphantha deserti is a solitary form 3 to 8 inches tall, covered with whitish spines with red-brown tips. The number of radial spines, 20 to 25, is a distinctive character. The flowers are pink, rose, yellowish, or straw-colored (pl. 8, *a*). The flower color seems to differ from area to area.

This species has a more easterly distribution in the Mojave Desert than its near relative, the Foxtail Cactus, and may be observed on rocky hillsides at elevations of 1,500 to 6,000 feet in ranges between Baker and Needles and north into Inyo County. Good colonies may be seen between Cima and Ivanpah and in the Lanfair Valley to the southeast.

Foxtail Cactus *(Coryphantha alversonii)*

A. H. Alverson, prospectors' supplier and desert 'raveler out of early San Bernardino, discovered this plant on one of his wagon expeditions about 1890 and sent specimens to the United States National Herbarium. It is now recognized as one of the most attractive cacti of the Joshua Tree National Monument. Not only can it be touched with safety, but it produces lovely flowers.

The species is distinguished from its near relative, *Coryphantha deserti*, by its more numerous brown-tipped central spines (12-16) and shorter tubercules. The plants are commonly larger and often have several heads (pl. 8, *c*). The ranges of the two species hardly overlap, for *C. alversonii* is characteristic of the south Mojave Desert, largely within the Joshua Tree National Monument, where the plant is now protected. The Foxtail Cactus does not survive well in cultivation, and in the past thousands of plants were dug up, only to die in coastal gardens. Some of the best remaining colonies may be seen in the Monument around White Tank south of Twentynine Palms, and near Old Dale.

Arizona Pincushion Cactus (*Coryphantha arizonica*)

This is a rare plant in California and in part overlaps the range of *Coryphantha deserti*. It may be distinguished easily, however, by its much larger flowers (pl 8, *d*), and by the smaller number of radial spines (fewer than 20) which allow the tubercles to be seen clearly. The heads are usually solitary and hemispherical, 3 to 4 inches high.

Coryphantha arizonica must be sought in California in easternmost San Bernardino County within 50 to 60 miles of the Nevada boundary, in the New York and Castle Mountains, and between Cima and Goffs in the Lanfair Valley area. It may be found among piñon and juniper in the vicinity of Mitchell's Caverns in the Providence Mountains. During flowering season in May and June the otherwise rather obscure plants are strikingly evident.

Coastal Fishhook Cactus; Nipple Cactus
(*Mammillaria dioica*)

Mammillaria is a large genus of nipple or pincushion cacti sometimes recognized as containing more than 200 species. Most of them are rather small single or clustered plants, and many have hooked spines. Most of the kinds of *Mammillaria* occur in Mexico. Several extend into Arizona, but only two into California. As with *Echinocereus,* some manuals and floras group other related genera such as *Phellosperma* and *Coryphantha* under *Mammillaria,* but for our purposes it seems more effective to recognize the distinctive features of these under different names.

Mammillaria dioica is a plant of San Diego County west of the Borrego Desert. It is often common in the seacoast chaparral and may be observed at the Cabrillo National Monument at Point Loma (pl. 8, e). A somewhat more robust form than the coastal one extends inland through the mountains below 5,000 feet to the western edge of the Colorado Desert. It may be seen in Sentenac Canyon below Julian in the *Opuntia bigelovii* association.

Distinctive characters of *Mammillaria* are often small and should be studied with a hand lens. The outer parts of the flower in *M. dioica,* for example, are not ciliate as in *M. microcarpa,* and there are small bristles in the axils of the tubercles. The stigma lobes are green. The specific name refers to an interesting character in which the flowers are partly dioecious. Some plants, that is, have flowers which are only male or only female.

Desert Fishhook Cactus (*Mammillaria microcarpa*)

This species is characteristically an Arizona plant that occurs within California only in the far western edges of our deserts near the Colorado River. Its only reported range within the state is in the Whipple Mountains near Parker Dam, where much of the characteristic Arizona flora crosses the river, including the Giant Saguaro.

Mammillaria microcarpa is superficially similar to both *M. dioica* and *Phellosperma tetrancistra*. It lacks the corky-based seeds of the latter and the auxiliary bristles of both. It has only 11 to 30 radial spines. Its lavender flowers, which usually appear in April, have distinctive ciliate margins on the perianth segments, and the stigmas are of a paler color than the green of *M. dioica* (fig. 23).

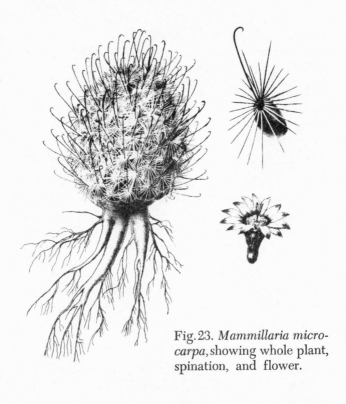

Fig. 23. *Mammillaria microcarpa*, showing whole plant, spination, and flower.

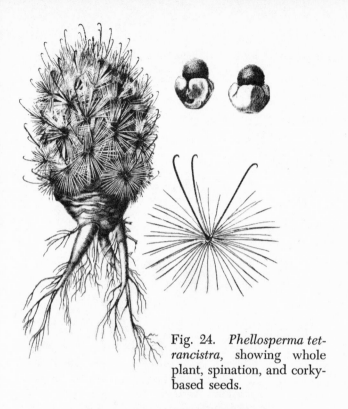

Fig. 24. *Phellosperma tetrancistra*, showing whole plant, spination, and corky-based seeds.

Cork-seeded Fishhook Cactus
(*Phellosperma tetrancistra*)

This fishhook cactus superficially resembles *Mammillaria dioica*, but has a much broader range, larger flowers, and different spine and seed characters. It has a large number of delicate white radial spines (30 to 60) and four long black centrals, at least one of which is hooked. The flowers are pink to purplish and much more showy than those of *M. dioica* (pl. 8, f). The seeds are especially interesting and are the distinguishing feature of the genus, for they are borne on a relatively large corky base (fig. 24). The plants are as attractive in fruit as in flower, for the cylindrical spineless fruits are bright red and project between the tubercles against the white spines. They yield a pleasant acid taste and have the Spanish name "chilitos" (fig. 25).

Fig. 25.   Typical fruit of *Mammillaria* and *Phellosperma*.

Although widely distributed, *P. tetrancistra* is a scarce plant within its habitat. It favors granitic hillslopes and alluvial fans usually below 2,000 feet throughout the Colorado and southern Mojave deserts and on into western Arizona. It is often associated with *Ferocactus acanthodes, Opuntia bigelovii,* and *O. echinocarpa.* Good places to look for this species are in the vicinity of the Devil's Playground near Kelso. This is the large form. In Sentenac Canyon below Banner on Highway 78, and in the boulder-filled canyon east of Jacumba on Highway 80 plants are quite numerous. A distinctive dwarf form only one and one-half inches high at maturity occurs in rock crevices at Ord Mountain and in the New York Mountains.

CACTUS BOOKS AND CLUBS

This is the only book especially on California cacti to have appeared for thirty years. *California Cactus*, by E. M. Baxter, published in 1935, has long been out of print. For those who desire a more comprehensive handbook of the American cacti, the writer's *How to Know the Cacti*, 1963, is available from the Wm. C. Brown Co., Dubuque, Iowa.

Most of the available literature on cacti can be obtained through the Abbey Garden Press, 18007 Topham Street, Reseda, California. The following titles may be of interest to California cactus enthusiasts: *Cacti of San Diego County*, by Lindsay; *Cacti of the Southwest*, by Earle; *Cacti for the Amateur*, by Haselton; *Cactaceae*, by Marshall and Bock; *The Cactaceae* (4 vols.), by Britton and Rose.

The Abbey Garden Press is publication headquarters for the bimonthly *Journal* of the Cactus and Succulent Society of America, which has been published for over thirty years. Persons interested in cacti will enjoy membership in this national society and attendance at its meetings and conventions. There are a number of affiliated cactus societies in California where those of similar interests meet to discuss their plants and pictures. Some of these clubs are in Sacramento, Oakland, San Jose, Bakersfield, Santa Monica, Los Angeles, Hawthorne, Gardena, Long Beach, Victorville, Riverside, Vista, San Diego, and El Centro.

GLOSSARY

arborescent — treelike.

areoles — specialized spots on the body of a cactus bearing hair, wool, glochids, spines, and sometimes leaves; potentially capable of new growth and the production of branches or flowers

axil — the point of divergence of a branch, a leaf, or a tubercle.

central spines — those arising from the center of the areole and more or less erect.

chaparral — a vegetation type of the Southwest characterized by dense, low, coarse brush with few or no trees, capable of rapid regeneration after fires.

ciliate — bearing a fringe of hairlike processes.

deciduous — falling away at maturity.

decumbent — reclining, but with the terminus ascending.

deflexed — bent, curved, or directed downward.

dioecious — plants or flowers in which one flower bears the male, staminate parts, and another bears the female, pistillate parts.

epiphytic — growing on another plant.

glochids — minute spines provided with retuse barbs, characteristic of *Opuntia* and usually found in large numbers in its areoles.

inferior ovary — an ovary situated below the insertion of the perianth segments.

obpyriform — inversely pear-shaped.

ovary — the fleshy basal part of the cactus flower which becomes the fruit.

perianth segments — those parts of the flower corresponding to the petals and sepals when distinction between these is not clear.

porrect — directed outward and forward.

proliferous — reproducing or regenerating freely by offsets.

radial spines — spines arising from the outer part of the areole and oriented radially.

rotate — wheel-shaped when open.

tubercles — protuberances from the fleshy body of the cacti in the form of low or high mounds, or of nipple-like structures.

tuberculate — beset with knobby projections or excrescences.

vascular system — the woody conductive tissue within the fleshy plant body.

INDEX